My Green Activity Book

Take out the Trash

It's important to take the time to sort your rubbish so things that can be recycled will be made into something new.

Correctly colour the dots to put each piece of rubbish in the right bin.

RUBBISH BIN

RECYCLING BIN

GARDEN WASTE BIN

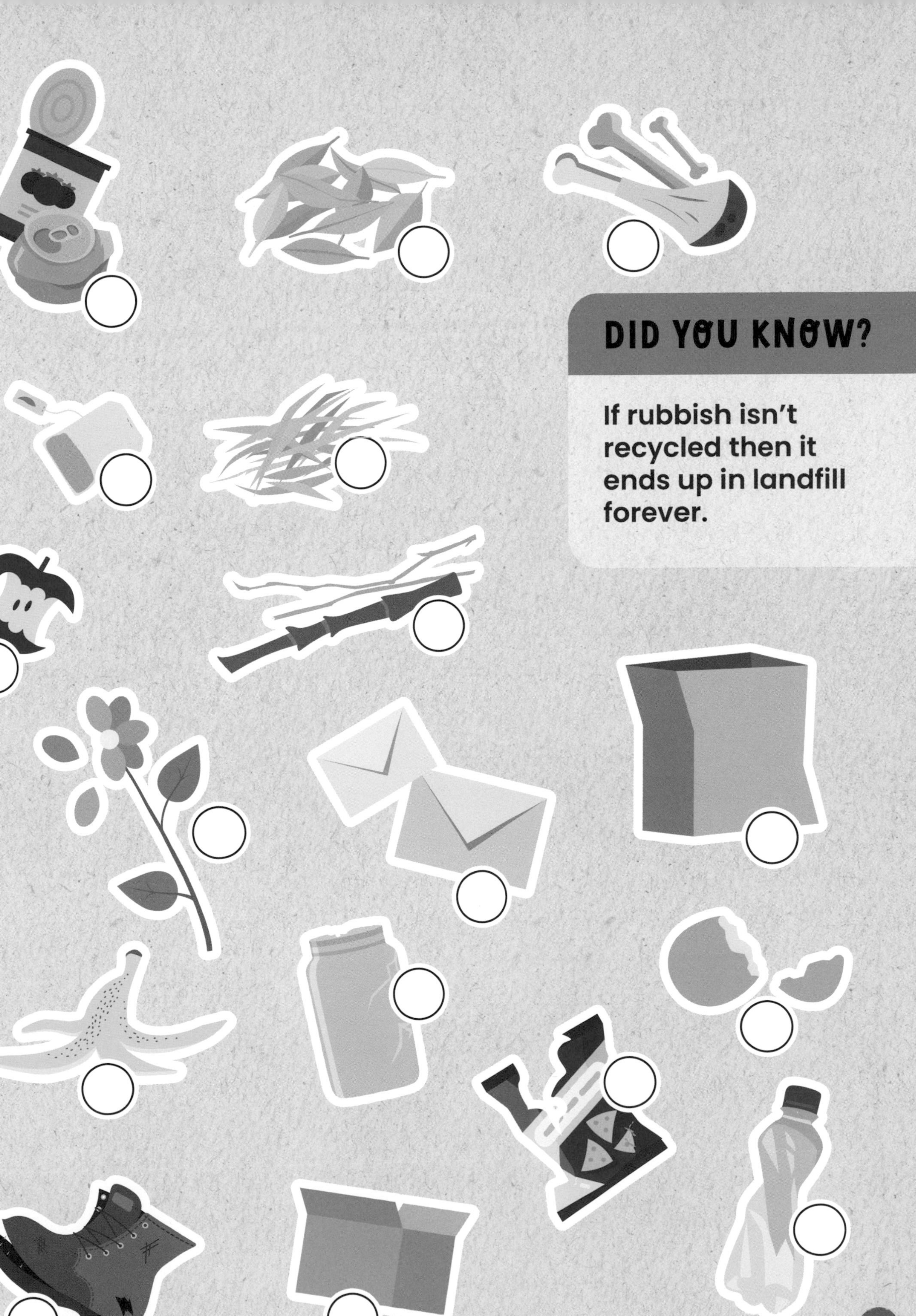

DID YOU KNOW?

If rubbish isn't recycled then it ends up in landfill forever.

Litter Labels

Cut out and colour these labels to stick on your bins, to make it even easier to recycle your rubbish!

RUBBISH

FOOD

GARDEN

RECYCLING

Waste Word Search

Can you find these rubbish-related words in the grid? Remember to look in all directions – up, down, across, backwards AND diagonally!

R	E	C	Y	D	E	D	L	S	A
L	E	R	E	S	C	E	C	O	L
A	L	U	C	O	E	O	I	M	P
N	G	H	S	R	L	R	N	A	E
D	A	S	G	E	C	G	A	R	L
F	R	A	D	N	Y	S	G	N	C
I	O	R	G	A	C	N	R	I	Y
L	A	T	S	O	P	M	O	C	C
L	D	C	U	R	U	G	A	N	E
S	E	R	L	E	C	U	D	E	R

RECYCLE
ECO
REDUCE
LANDFILL
COMPOST
ORGANIC
REUSE
TRASH
UPCYCLE

Community Clean-up

Help to keep your local area clean and tidy! Trace a path around the town without taking your pencil off the page or touching either side of the path. Collect all the litter from the list along the way.

START

LITTER LIST

SCHOOL
CAFE
Juice
Water
FINISH

Knock, Knock!

Let your friends and family know if they're allowed in your room today by making this handy door hanger.

YOU WILL NEED

- Scissors
- Coloured pens
- Card
- Glue

1. Cut out the door hanger, snipping along the dotted lines.
2. Colour in each side and add some decorations to make your door hanger shine.
3. Stick the underside of the door hanger onto card and when the glue is dry, cut it out again.
4. Fold the door hanger in half and stick both sides together.
5. When the glue is dry, place your door hanger over the handle to your room.

Make sure you complete the activity on page 10 before cutting out your door hanger!

The Right Route

It's time for a trip to the Toy and Book Library! Which is the quickest route to take? Add up the numbers along each path and pick the one with the lowest total.

A B C D E

2 5 4 6 1 3 3 1 2 1 2 3 4 2 1 4 7 4 2 5 2 1 2 2 3 5

LIBRARY

DID YOU KNOW?

It's much better for the environment if you can leave the car at home and walk or ride instead.

Share, Swap and Spot

Sharing is caring! Can you spot the things from the panel on the shelves in the Toy and Book Library?

Awesome Upcycling

Use your design skills and colouring pencils to upcycle these old items and make them shiny and new again!

Splish, Splash, Spot!

Can you spot six differences between these shower scenes? Colour a water drop for each difference you find.

Pull the Plug!

To save water, stop filling the bathtub and start taking a quick shower. Which plug cord should you pull to empty the bath?

DID YOU KNOW?

Water is precious, so it's much better to take a quick shower than have a long soak in the bath.

A

B

C

D

E

Fabric Fantastic

Design your own tote! Draw, colour and decorate it with a cool picture or a catchy slogan, or both!

DID YOU KNOW?

Plastic is bad for our planet, so it's a good idea to carry a reusable fabric bag instead.

Make sure you complete the activity on page 18 before cutting out your stencil!

I AM AN
ECO
ZOOMer

Here's a template for you to create your very own Eco Zoomers tote bag! Cut along the dotted lines, trace it onto a fabric bag (make sure you ask permission first), then use fabric paint to colour it in.

Light the Way

Make your way through the house, passing each lightbulb along the way. Colour them green as you go!

START

DID YOU KNOW?

To make your home more eco-friendly, it's a bright idea to turn off the lights when you're not using them.

FINISH

Planet Earth Patches

Show your eco side! Colour in these logos and slogans and then add some of your own. You could cut them out and stick them onto your school folder or bedroom door.

RECYCLE

LOVE our PLANET

KEEP the OCEAN CLEAN
Save the WILD
NO EXCUSE FOR SINGLE USE
I ♡ EARTH

Arms Around the World

We need to work together if we're going to make a difference and save our planet. Create some paper bunting to hang around your room and give planet Earth a great big hug!

YOU WILL NEED

- Scissors
- Pencil
- Card
- Colouring pens
- String or a shoelace
- Tape

1. Cut out the template, snipping along the dotted lines.
2. Trace around the template lots of times onto card, then colour in the people before cutting them out.
3. Turn the people over and place them in a row so their hands are touching.
4. Tape the people, hands touching, along a length of string or shoelaces tied together.
5. Hang the bunting around your room.

Answer page

PAGES 2–3

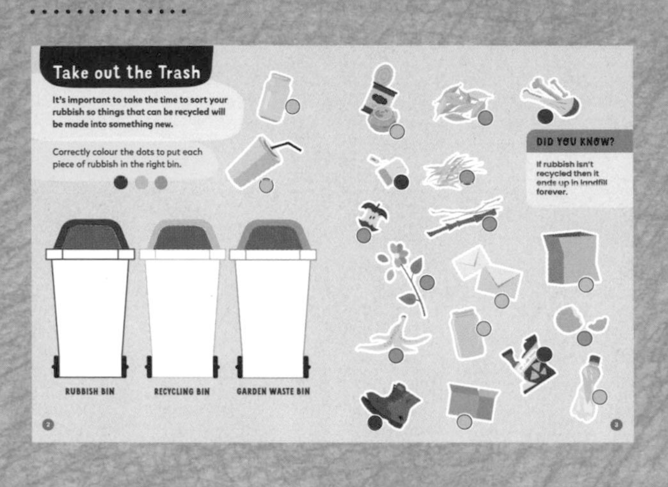

PAGE 5

PAGES 6–7

PAGE 10

Path **B** is the quickest route.

PAGE 11

PAGE 14

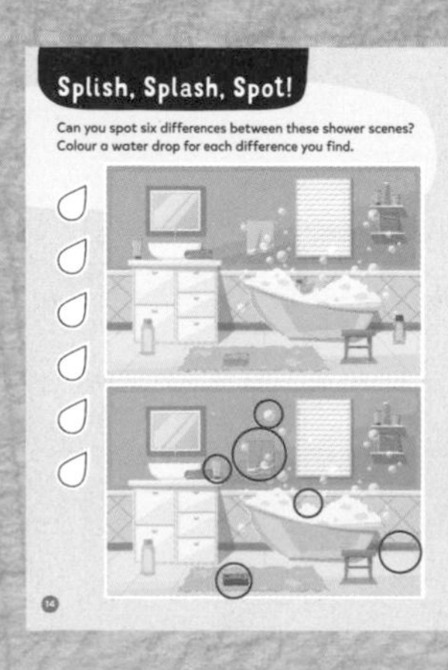

PAGE 15

Pull plug cord **E** to empty the bath.

PAGES 18–19